CELINE DION THE COLOUR OF MY LOVE

Wise Publications
London / New York / Paris / Sydney / Copenhagen / Madrid

IMP

International Music Publications Limited
Southend Road, Woodford Green, Essex IG8 8HN, England

Distributors:

Music Sales Limited
8/9 Frith Street, London W1V 5TZ, England.
Music Sales Pty Limited
120 Rothschild Avenue, Rosebery, NSW2018, Australia.

Order No.AM936430
ISBN 0-7119-5697-9

Visit the Music Sales' Internet Music Shop at
http://www.musicsales.co.uk

International Music Publications Limited
Southend Road, Woodford Green, Essex IG8 8HN, England.
International Music Publications Limited
25 Rue D'Hauteville, 75010 Paris, France.
International Music Publications Gmbh, Germany
Marstallstrasse 8, D-80539 Munchen.

Order Ref. 3821A
ISBN 1-85909-356-6

Music arranged by Roger Day
Music processed by Paul Ewers Music Design

Printed in the United Kingdom by
Page Bros, Norwich

THE POWER OF LOVE

Words & Music by C.deRouge, G.Mende, J.Rush & S.Applegate.

E♭
fr3
as I look in your eyes.
A♭
fr4
I hold on to your bo - dy,
Fm
and feel each move you make,
D♭
your voice is warm and ten - der, a love that

A♭/C
E♭
fr3
I could not for - sake.
A♭
fr4
'Cause I'm your la - - - dy,
D♭
and you are my man,
when - ev - er you reach
B♭m
for me,
I'll do all that I can.

E♭
fr3
1.
2.
2. Lost is how I'm
We're head - ing for
A♭
fr4
D♭
some - thing,
some-where I've ne - ver been,
B♭m
some - times I am fright - ened but I'm rea - dy to learn
To Coda
E♭
fr3
D♭
A♭
fr4
of the pow - er of love.

D♭
E♭
A♭
fr3
fr4
The sound of your heart beat - ing
made it clear sud-den-
Fm
ly,
the feel-ing that I can't go on
D.%. al Coda
is light years a - way.
'Cause I'm your la -
Coda
The pow - er of love,

Verse 2:
Lost is how I'm feeling
Lying in your arms,
When the world outside's too much to take,
That all ends when I'm with you.
Even though there may be times
It seems I'm far away,
Never wonder where I am
'Cause I am always by your side.

Misled

Words & Music by Peter Zizzo & Jimmy Bralower.

Fm
G7
Cm9
F9
I guess you ne - ver can tell oh I learned ear - ly, ne - ver to ig - nore the signs,
A♭
Fm
G7
A♭
you'll be for - gi - ven, it ain't worth that much to my mind lo - vin' you so ea -
(𝄋. see block lyric)
not on D.𝄋.
E♭
Cm7
Am7(♭5)
- sy it's hard to say good - bye, but if that's the way it goes, it goes.
Fm
G7
Cm7
Fm
G7
Just a page in my his - to - ry, just an - oth - er one of those mys -

Cm7
Fm
G7
Cm7
fr3
- te-ries, one more lo - ver that used to be, if you
Dm7add4
To Coda
N.C.
think you're in my head, you been se-ri-ous-ly mis-led.
Cm7
F9
A♭
fr4
Fm
G7
Cm7
F9
I get on with my life, and you're not on my mind, and I took

A♭
fr4
Fm
G7
half the time to get ov - er you.
Cm
fr3
D.%. al Coda
Coda
N.C.
Fm
G7
se - ri - ous - ly mis - led. Just a page in my his -
Cm7
fr3
Fm
G7
Cm7
fr3
- to - ry, just an - oth - er one of those mys - te - ries,

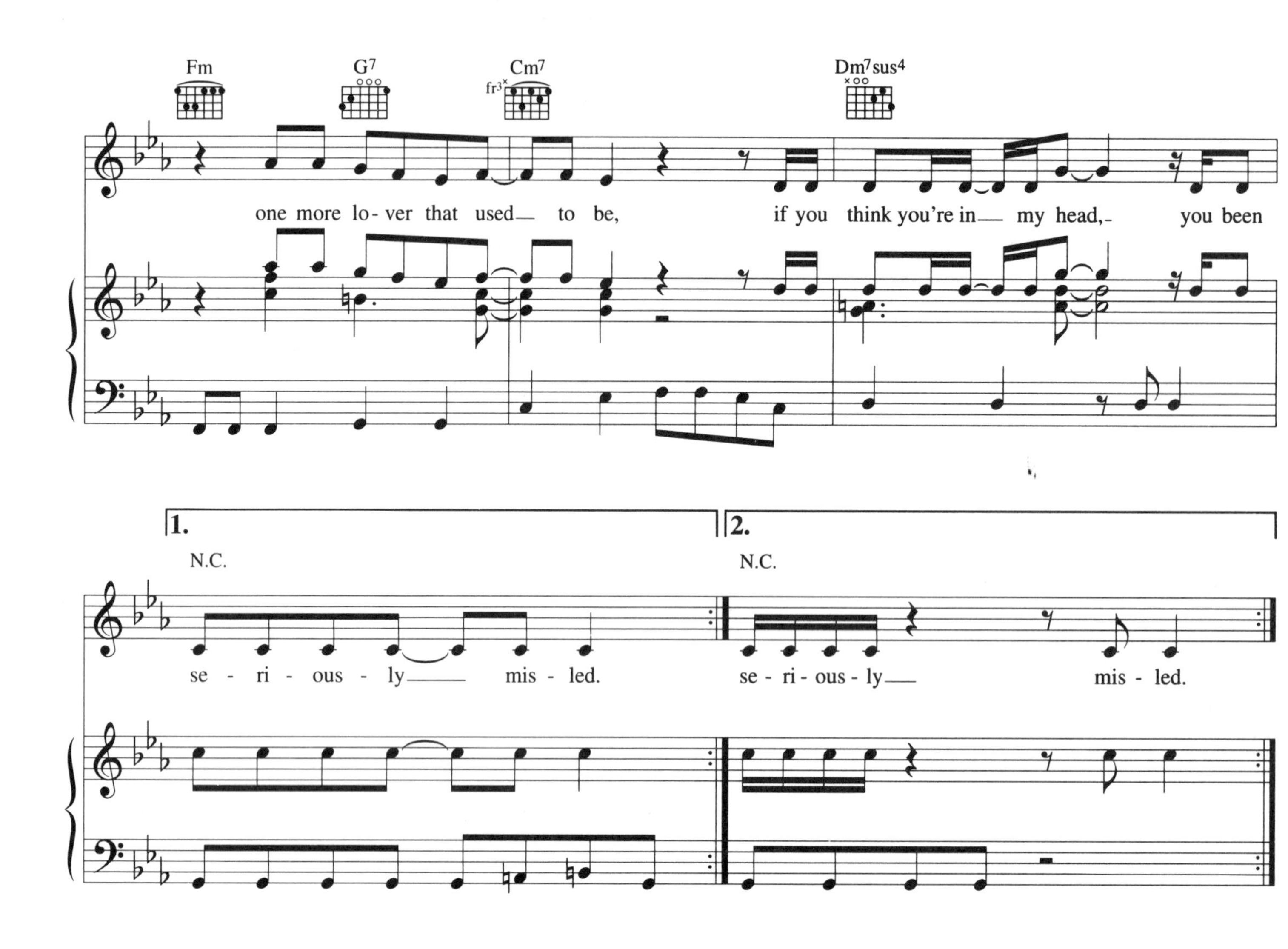

Verse 2:
Loving somebody
Ain't your average nine to five.
It takes conviction,
It takes a will to survive.
I'm not somebody
Who commits the crime and leaves the scene,
But when I've been dissed
I don't spend much time
On what might've been.

I'm not about self-pity
Your love did me wrong
Now I'm moving,
Moving on.

Verse 3: (**D.%.**)
I'm not about self pity
Your love did me wrong
So I'm moving,
Moving on.

Think Twice

Words & Music by Andy Hill & Pete Sinfield.

Dm
Gm7
fr3
3
I look in your eyes, there's a dis - tant light
3
C
Am7
B♭
and you and I know there'll be a storm to - night.
Gm7
fr3
C
This is get - ting ser - i - ous,
Gm7
fr3
C
B♭/D
C/E
are you think - in' 'bout you or us. Don't say

F
B♭
C
B♭/D
C/E
F
Am7
what you're a - bout to say,
look back be - fore you leave my
B♭
C
F
B♭
C
life.
Be sure be - fore you close that door,
be - fore you roll
Gm7
fr3
1.
B♭
F
those dice,
ba - by think twice.
Gm7
fr3
2.
B♭
Dm
2. Ba - by think
ba - by think twice.

Gm7
fr3
Dm7
Gm7
fr3
Gm7
fr3
B♭
C
Gm7
fr3
B♭
3
Ba - by this is ser - i - ous,
are you think - in' a - bout
C
you or us?
Ba - by.
Don't say
F
B♭
C
B♭/D
C/E
what you're a - bout to say,
look back

Verse 2:
Baby think twice, for the sake of our love
For the memory,
For the fire and the faith
That was you and me.
Babe I know it ain't easy
When your soul cries out for higher ground,
'Cause when you're halfway up
You're always halfway down.

But baby this is serious
Are you thinking 'bout you or us?

Only One Road

Words & Music by Peter Zizzo.

Dm7
Gm7
Cm7
F7
Dm7
this one day and ma - ny dreams lost a - long the
Gm7
E dim
B♭
D7
Gm
way, haunt me still, I guess they al - ways will.
E♭
A♭/E♭
E♭
B♭/D
Cm7
F7
When love was too much to bear, I just left it there.
1.
2, 3.
B♭
Gm7
2. Here I There is on - ly one road I'm walk - ing,

E♭maj7 F/E♭ Dm7 E♭ B♭/D Cm7
on - ly one life - time, one heart to guide me.
B♭ Gm7 E♭maj7
On - ly one road I'm walk - ing, but I'm gon - na run
F/E♭ Dm7 Gm7 Cm7 F
back, I'm gon - na run back, 'cause I need you right here be -
To Coda
D.%. al Coda
Cdim B♭ E♭ A♭/E♭ E♭ F7sus4 F7
side me. 3. I can

Coda
A♭
fr4
E♭
fr3
Cm7(♭5)
B♭/F
F/E♭
B♭/D
Gm7
fr3
rall.
G
a tempo
C
Am7
Fmaj7
On - ly one road I'm walk - ing, on - ly one life - time,
G/F
Em7
F
C/E
Dm7
C
one heart to guide me, on - ly one road I'm

Am7
Fmaj7
G/F
walk - ing
but I'm gon - na
run
back, I'm gon - na
Em7
Am7
Dm7
G
3
run
back, 'cause I need you right
here
be -
C
Am7
Fmaj7
side
me.
'Cause I'm gon- na
run
G/F
Em7
E♭dim
Dm7
back, I'm gon- na
run
back, 'cause ba - by I need
you

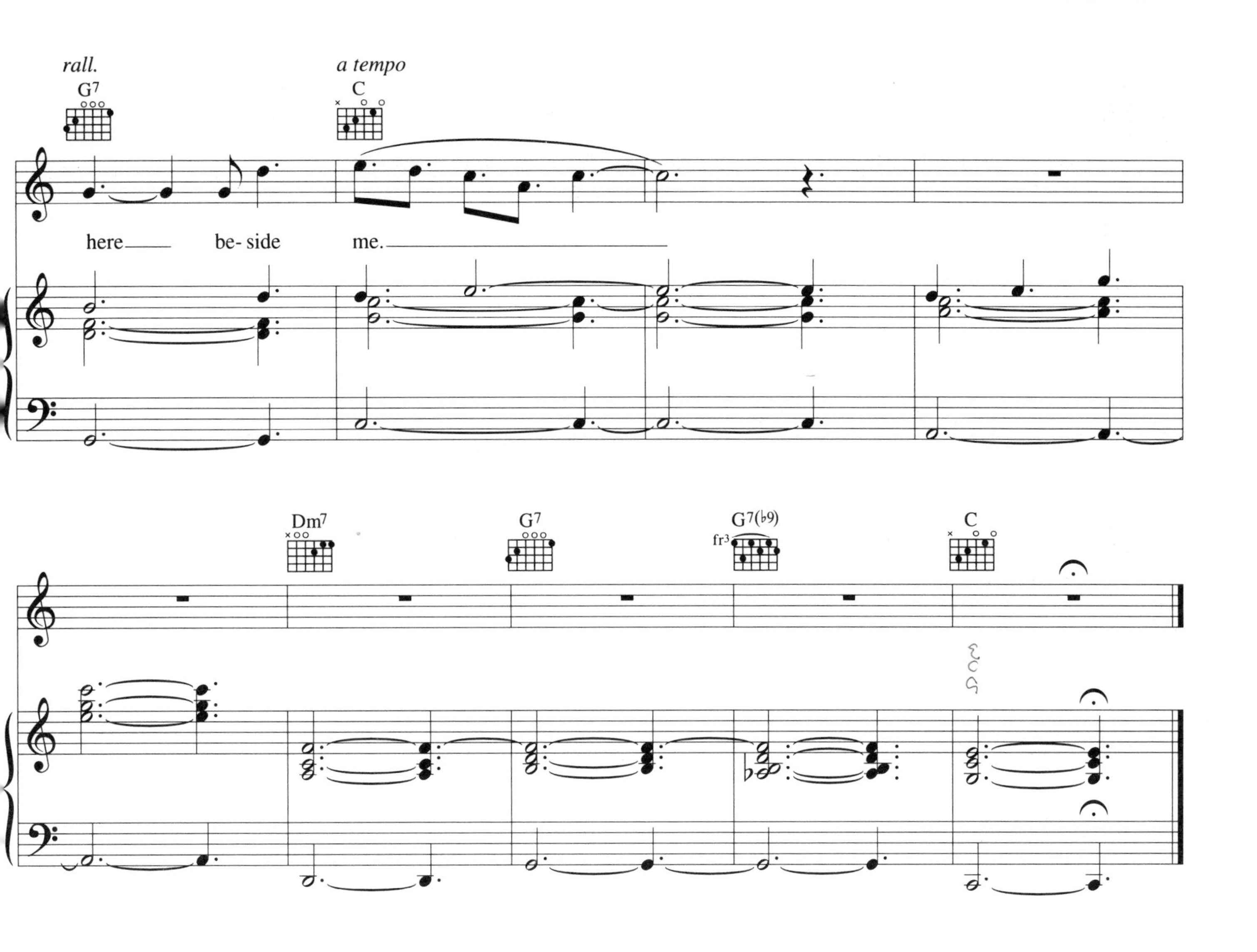

Verse 2:
Here I stand, face to face
With this heart of mine
Living without you
I only fall behind.
We had a love most people never find
All this time I never realised
And the courage I finally found
Has made me turn around.

Verse 3:
I can still hear the song
Of your laughter,
I can still taste the sorrow
Of your tears
We said goodbye but our hearts did not hear
Now my love there's nothing left to fear.
With all my heart put me through
It leads me back to you.

Everybody's Talkin' My Baby Down

Words & Music by Russ De Salvo & Arnie Roman.

Gmaj7
F♯m7
fool - in' with your heart girl, but I know how he makes me feel
Am7/D
fr5
D7
Gmaj7
F♯m7
and I don't need an - y oth - er proof, they
Em7
F♯m7
Em7/A
just don't un - der - stand, they don't know the truth.
Bm7
Em7
Mom-ma says he's bad for me, Pop-pa says I'll be sor - ry,

Gmaj7
Em7
F♯m7
ev - 'ry - bo - dy's talk - in' my ba - by down,
Bm7
Em7
and all my friends doubt him, tell me I should live with - out him,
Gmaj7
Em7/A
F♯/A♯
ev - 'ry - bo - dy's talk - in' my ba - by down.
Bm7
Em7
My sis - ters and my broth - ers tell me I should find an - oth - er,

Gmaj7
Em7/A
F♯/A♯
ev - 'ry - bo - dy's talk - in' my ba - by down.
Bm7
B7sus4
B7
Em7
Oh but they can't feel his touch, they can't
F♯m7
Gmaj7
B7sus4
B7
feel his kiss, they don't know what it's like to be loved like this.
Em7
F♯m7
I don't care a - bout their point of view 'cause it's

Em7/A
un - der - stood when the love is good, noth - in' else is gon - na do.
Bm7
Em7
Mom - ma says he's bad for me, Pop - pa says I'll be sor - ry,
Gmaj7
Em7
F♯m7
ev - 'ry - bo - dy's talk - in' my ba - by down,
Bm7
Em7
and all my friends doubt him, tell me I should live with - out him,

Verse 2:
He's not like the others,
Nobody wants to see it,
They don't even want to try.
Judge a book by its cover
And you'll never know the story,
There's so much more than meets the eye.
Oh and I know his heart is true,
I don't need anyone to tell me what to do.

Next Plane Out

Words & Music by Diane Warren.

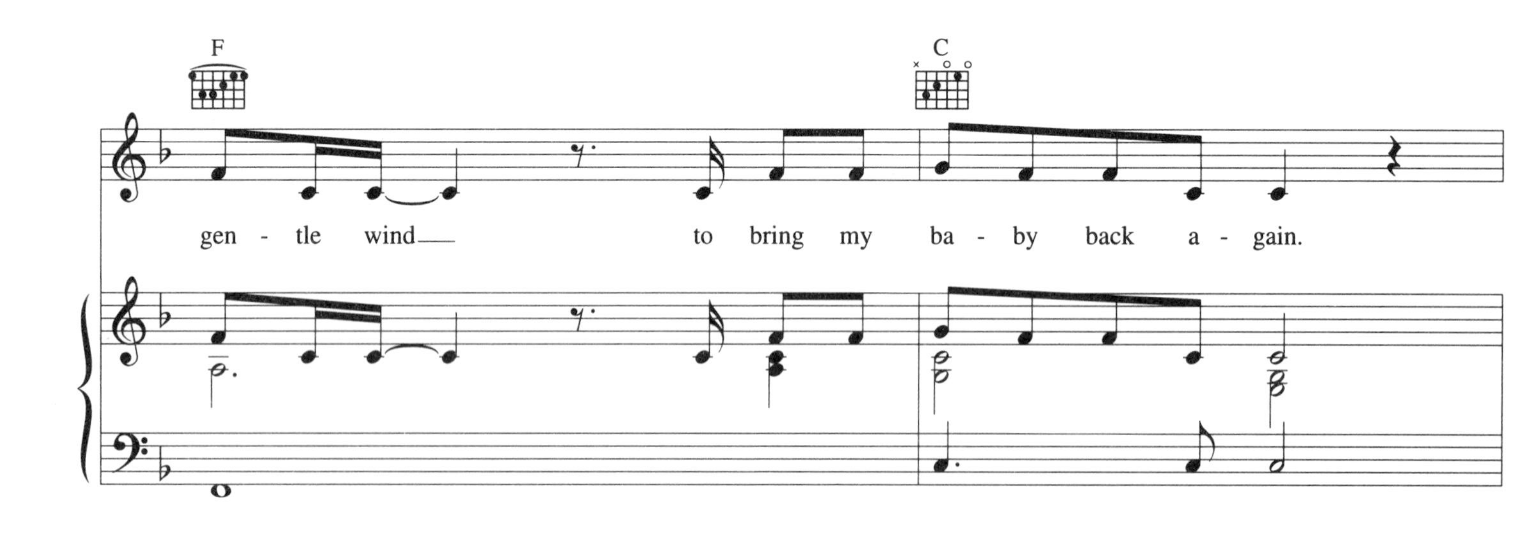

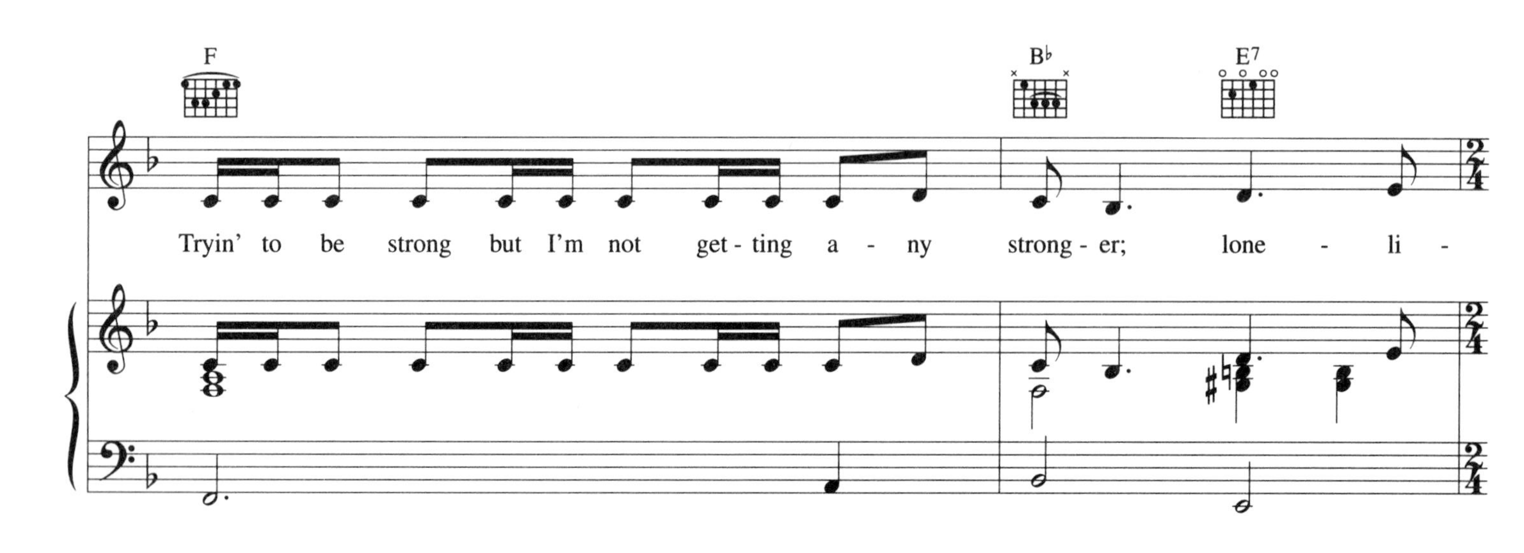

Am7
C sus4
C
ness is tear - ing a - part this heart of mine.
B♭maj7
F/A
Gm7
fr3
F/A
I lie a - wake 'cause I can't take an - oth - er night lone - ly,
B♭maj7
F/A
Gm7
fr3
it's been too long, I can't hold on no more. Leav - in' on the
F
Gm7
fr3
next plane out 'cause I got - ta see my ba - by. It's

F
Gm7
fr3
C
been too long since I held him in my arms and I just won't
F
Gm7
fr3
B♭
sleep at night till he's sleep-in here be-side me,
E♭
fr3
C sus4
F
1.
B♭
here be-side me a-gain.
2.
B♭
F
B♭
I got-ta be with my ba-by.

A♭
fr4
E♭/G
fr3
B♭
Got - ta be with him, got - ta be by his side,
G♭
C7sus4
fr3
a tempo
gon - na be with him my heart's made up my mind. I'm leav - ing on the
F♯
G♯m7
fr4
next plane out 'cause I got - ta see my ba - by, it's
F♯
G♯m7
fr4
been too long since I held him in my arms and I just won't

F♯
G♯m7
fr4
B
sleep at night
till he's sleep-in' here be - side me,
E
C♯sus4
fr4
F♯
G♯m7
fr4
here be - side me,
it's
F♯
G♯m7
fr4
B
C♯sus4
fr4
been too long
since I held him in my arms,
then I just won't
F♯
G♯m7
fr4
B
sleep at night,
till he's sleep-in' here be - side me,

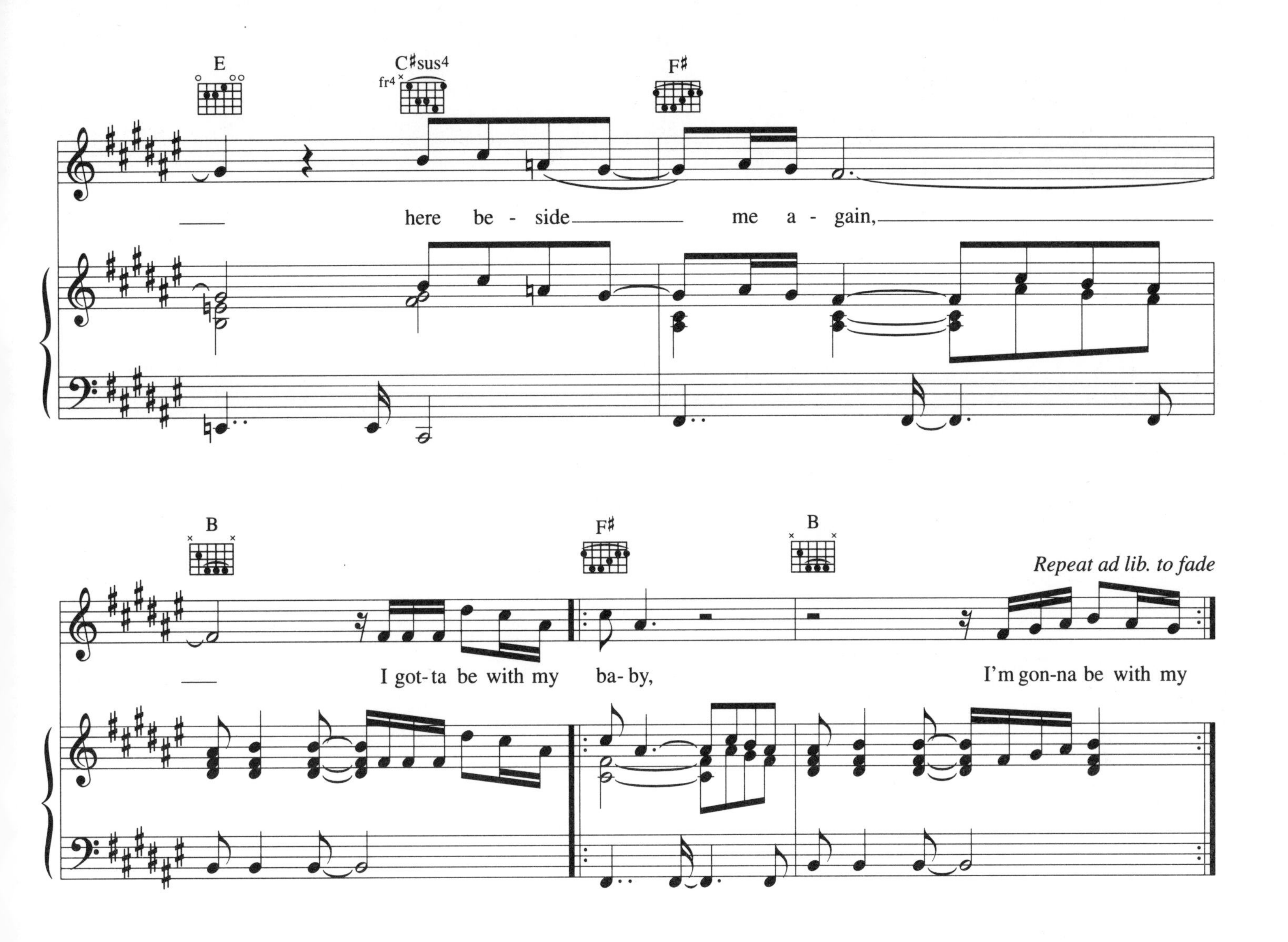

Verse 2:
Talkin' on the phone but that don't make it any better
Nothing's gonna ease this pain until I'm in his arms again.
Runnin' down the stairs, there's a taxi that's waiting for me
Loneliness, I'm gonna leave you far behind.

I'd walk for days through pouring rain, anything to be with him.
It's been too long, I can't be strong no more.

Additional lyrics to fade:
Gonna take the next plane or the next train
Gotta get there, gotta see my baby.
And nothing's gonna stop me from leaving this time.
Leavin' on the next plane out…

Real Emotion

Words & Music by Diane Warren.

F
Cm9
show me you love me, that ain't gon - na win this heart of mine.
Fsus4
F
All the dia - monds you can buy won't im - press me,
(Verse 2 see block lyric)
Fsus4
F
F11
Fsus4
pret - ty words ain't gon - na prove your love.
I need more than just to - kens
F
Cm9
of af - fec - tion, I'm not ask - ing for too much now ba - by,

A♭
fr4
Gm7
fr3
I don't need no fancy cars,
just need some-
A♭
fr4
C11
- thing from the heart.
Yeah, yeah, yeah, I
B♭
F
Gm7
fr3
need real e - mo - tion,
feel, got - ta
F
F11
B♭
Dm7
feel it in - side, give me
that real e - mo - tion 'cause I

Cm9
1.
need some, need to feel some to - night, give me a love that's gen-u-ine.
B♭
F
Gm7
fr3
Real e - mo - tion, real e - mo -
F
2.
- tion. give me a love that's gen - u - ine. Not a cheap
F
i - mi - ta - tion of love, I need some - thing that's real, I can feel in my heart ba - by.

B♭/F
F
I've been wait - ing so long, so long, for a love,
for a love, for a love that's strong.
Gm7
fr3
Yeah, I don't need
A♭
fr4
Gm7
fr3
A♭
fr4
no fan - cy cars, just need some - thing from the heart.
C11
Yeah, yeah, yeah, yeah, yeah. I

Verse 2:
Show me something that my heart can believe in
Imitation love don't mean a thing
Baby it's got to be the real thing or nothing
Show me what it's gonna be now baby.
I'm not asking much from you
Just a love that's deep and true, yeah…

When I Fall In Love

Music by Victor Young. Words by Edward Heyman.

D♭
B♭m
C♭7
D♭
/C♭
B♭sus4
B♭7
rest - less world like this is, love is end - ed be - fore it's be - gun, and too
E♭m
E♭m(maj7)
E♭m
To Coda
Fm/E♭
A♭13
fr4
ma - ny moon - light kiss - es seem to cool in the warmth of the sun.
D♭
G♭m/D♭
D♭
G♭m/D♭
D♭
G♭m/D♭
B♭7/D♭
E♭m
A♭7(♭9)
fr4
When I give my heart, it will be com - plete - ly,
D♭
C♭7
B♭7aug
E♭m7
fr6
A♭11
A♭13(♭9)
fr3
or I'll ne - ver give my heart. And the

D♭
B♭m7
Gm7add9
C7(♭5)
Fm7
B♭7(♭9)
E♭m
C♭7
mo - ment I can feel that you feel that way too,
D♭/A♭
G♭m/A♭
B♭7/A♭
A♭11
A♭13(♭9)
D♭
A♭/B♭
E♭m7
D.%. al Coda
/A♭
is when I fall in love with you.
Coda
A♭11
B♭11
E♭
A♭m/E♭
E♭
sun. When I give my heart
E♭
A♭m/D♭
C7aug
Fm7
B♭7(♭9)
E♭
Fm7
Gm7
A♭
C7aug
C7
it will be com - plete - ly, or I'll nev - er give my

Fm7 B♭9 B♭7(♭9) E♭ Cm7 A♭ D7(♭5)
heart. And the mo - ment I can feel that you
Gm7add4 C7aug Fm D♭7 E♭ A♭m/E♭
feel that way too, rall. is when I fall in
Fm7 B♭11 G♭/D♭ C♭m/D♭ D♭7(♭9)
love rall. when I fall in love,
E♭/B♭ A♭m/B♭ C7aug Fm7/B♭ B♭7 E♭ F/E♭ E♭
rall. when I fall in love with you.

Love Doesn't Ask Why

Words & Music by Philip Galdston, Barry Mann & Cynthia Weil.

E♭
B♭
Cm
love does - n't think twice, it can come all at once
Fm
E♭/B♭
B♭
or whis - per from a dis - tance. 1. Don't
(Verse 2 see block lyric)
Cm
A♭
ask me if this feel - ing's right or wrong, it does - n't
B♭/D
E♭
B♭/D
have to make much sense, it just has to be this strong 'cause

Cm
Fm
when you're in my arms I un - der - stand we
E♭/A♭
B♭/E♭
E♭/A♭
B♭/E♭
don't have a voice when our hearts make the choi - ces, there's no
A♭
1.
A♭
B♭
2.
A♭
B♭
plan, it… it's not in our hands. we can try.
E♭
B♭
Cm
Love does - n't ask why, it speaks from the heart

Fm
E♭/A♭
B♭
E♭
B♭
Cm
and nev - er ex - plains. Don't you know that love does - n't think twice,
Fm
E♭/B♭
B♭
it can come all at once or whis - per from a dis - tance. So let's
A♭
E♭/G
Fm7
B♭
take what we found and wrap it a - round us.
G♭
D♭
E♭m
A♭m
G♭/C♭
Love does - n't ask why it speaks from the heart and nev - er ex - plains
fr3
fr4

Verse 2:
Now I can feel what you're afraid to say,
If you give your soul to me.
Will you give too much away,
But we can't let this moment pass us by.
Can't question this chance
Or expect any answers.
We can try,
Maybe we can try.

Refuse To Dance

Words & Music by Charlie Dore & Danny Schogger.

Am
G/A
Dm/F
I con - fess,
I ne - ver ev - en
E/G♯
E(♭9)/G♯
knew the song, the or - ches - tra was play - ing.
Am
Am6
Am
G/A
See the cu - ties in their par - ty clothes, oh it's get - ting warm,
(Verse 2 see block lyric)
Am
Am6
Am
G/A
off the shoul - der, cut in - to the hip, like a u - ni - form.

Dm/F
E/G♯
fr2
E(♭9)/G♯
Do you think I'd want to tow the line, well now the line is bro - ken.
Am
Am6
Am
Re - fuse to dance, re - fuse to dance,
G/A
fr3
Am
Am6
re - fuse to dance, re - fuse
Am
G/A
fr3
Am
to dance. Re - fuse to dance,

Am6
Am
G/A
fr3
re - fuse to dance,
Am
Am6
Am
re - fuse to dance,
re - fuse to
To Coda
G/A
fr3
Fmaj7
G/F
3
dance.
See how they fol - low, (you say
C/E
Fmaj7
3
jump, they jump, you say turn, they turn)
look back in

Verse 2:
You said you're such a pretty thing,
You could make a mark.
I'll teach you all the steps you'll need,
Guide you through the dark.
Suddenly I thought I knew the song
The orchestra was playing.

I Remember L.A.

Words & Music by Tony Colton & Richard Wold.

E
B
seems a life - time a - go.
G♯m
fr4
We were stars on Sun - set
C♯m
fr4
Bou - le - vard.
E
What a mo -
F♯sus4
F♯
F♯sus4
F♯
- vie we made.

B
F♯
B
There were days in the sun
(Verse 2 see block lyric)
E
that have stayed for - ev - er
B
G♯m
young.
fr4
Nights when pas - sion was in -
C♯m
B/D♯
E
vin - ci - ble.
We thought love would nev - er

F♯sus4
F♯
B/D♯
fr4
E
F♯sus4
F♯
die. There were mo - ments in that life - time that my heart
B
E
still re - plays. There were mi - nutes, there were ho -
F♯sus4
F♯
B11
A/C♯
B/D♯
fr4
- urs, there were days. There are
E
F♯sus4
F♯
G♯m
fr4
E
mo- ments I still love you that same way.

Verse 2:
I remember goodbye,
I watched your plane out of sight.
Love was over, time to close the book,
Still I go back for one last look.

No Living Without Loving You

Words & Music by Diane Warren.

A♭
fr4
Fsus4
E♭add9
fr3
B♭/D
ev-en if you said good-bye now. Oh, the clock would-n't stop no,
Fm
D♭
A♭
fr4
Edim
that sun would still keep shin - ing down, dar - ling,
Fm
Cm7
fr3
B♭m
this world would still be spin - ning round, but ba - by,
/E♭
A♭
fr4
D♭/A♭
there would be just no liv - ing with - out lov - ing you,

A♭
D♭/A♭
A♭
how would I ev - er sur - vive.
Just no
D♭/A♭
D♭
E♭11
liv - ing with - out lov - ing you, would be like liv - ing with - out be - ing a - live, with - out
1.
A♭
D♭/A♭
A♭
D♭/A♭
A♭
E♭/G
you, with - out you.
2.
D♭/A♭
G♭
E♭11
with - out you ba - by. With - out

B♭
E♭
fr3
Cm7
fr3
you
there's no
liv - ing
with - out
lov - ing
you,
F11
B♭
E♭
fr3
oh
ba - by
in
my
life.
Just
Cm7
fr3
F11
E♭add9
fr3
love
me
babe,
oh
ba - by.
Oh,
the
Dm7
E♭11
clock
would - n't
stop,
no.
But
ba
-
by
there
would
be

Verse 2:
If you ever walk out this door,
What would I have left to live for?
What would there be left to do now,
What would I be without you now?
Oh, the clock wouldn't stop, no
Each day would go on just the same.
It wouldn't stop the sun and rain
But baby there would be...

Lovin' Proof

Words & Music by Diane Warren.

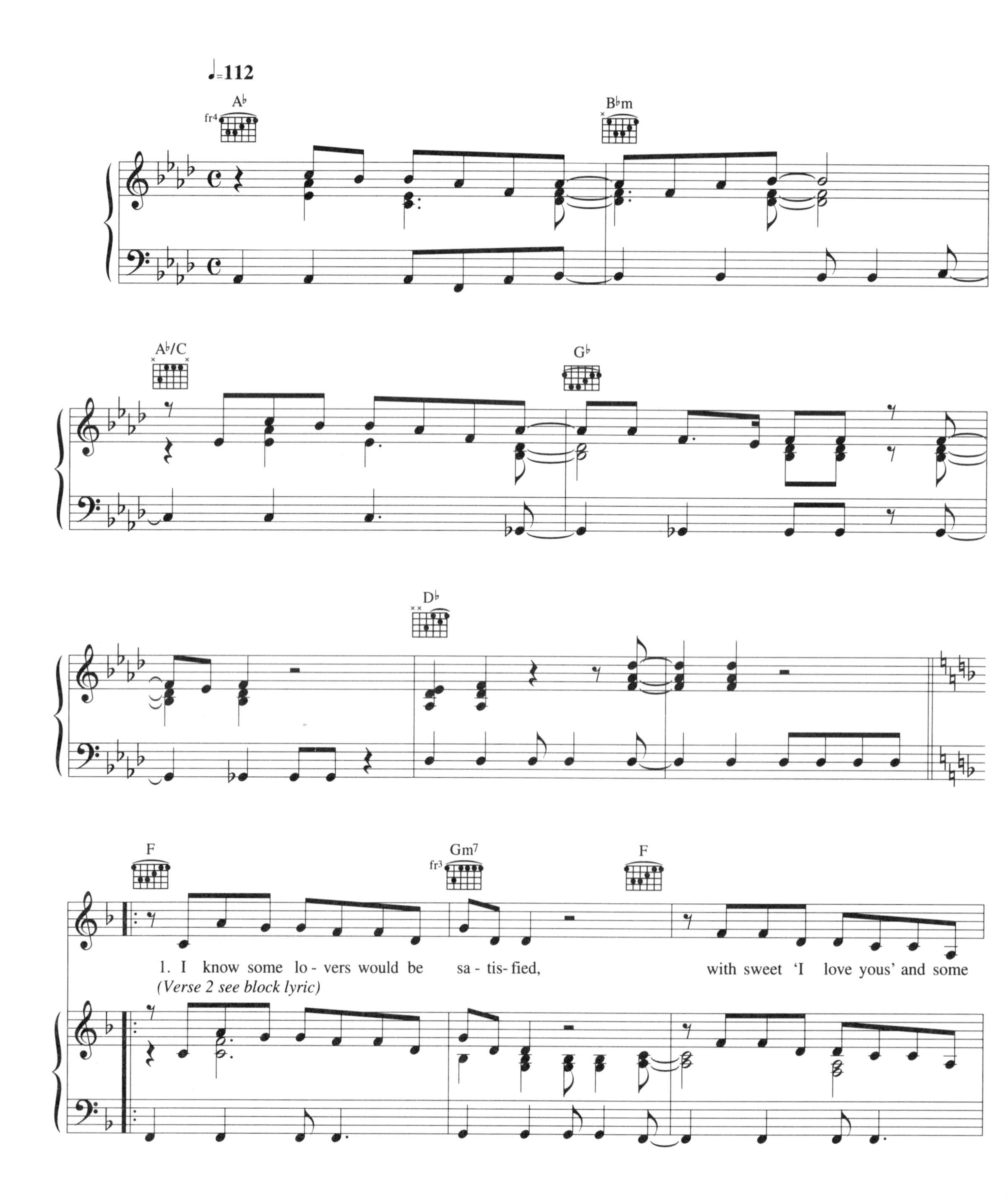

Gm7
F
pret - ty lines.
But that won't get you in this
Gm7
B♭
F/A
Gm7
heart of mine, no you'll ne - ver steal my heart a - way.
With just words,
A7
Dm
sweet words that you say
it's
Gm7
F
E♭
all in the things that you do,
I'm tell - ing you. If you want

A♭
fr4
B♭m
me to be - lieve that I'm the on - ly one you need, I need lov -
A♭/C
D♭
- in' proof. I need lov - in' proof ba - by hold
A♭
fr4
B♭m
me in your arms and show me some - thing from the heart, give me lov -
A♭/C
G♭maj7
fr4
To Coda
- in' proof. I need lov - - - in' proof.

D♭
1.
from you.
(baby)
2.
F
Gm7
fr3
I need lov - in' proof
(if the love is right)
I need lov - in' proof
(prove it to me all night)
I need lov - in' proof.
(from you)
D♭/A♭
B♭
'Cause you'll ne -

F/A
Gm7
A7
- ver steal my heart a - way.
With just words, sweet words that you say
Dm
Gm7
F
it's all in the things that you do,
E♭
D.𝄋. al Coda
I'm tell - ing you,
tell - ing you ba - by. If you want
⊕ Coda
D♭/A♭
from you.

Verse 2:
And if the love you got is strong and true
And if you love me like you say you do.
Your tender touch will tell the honest truth
And your kiss could never tell a lie.
'Cause I'd see it in your eyes,
There's one way to ease and doubt,
I tell you now.

Just Walk Away

Words & Music by Albert Hammond & Marti Sharron.

C♯m
A♯m♭5
G♯sus4
G♯7
fr4
I have lived and died, what I would-n't do just to be with you. I
C♯m
know I must for-get you to go on, I can't hold back my tears too
(Verse 2 see block lyric)
F♯m
C♯m
long though life won't be the same, I've got to take the blame and
A
G♯sus4
G♯7
C♯m
find the strength I need to let you go. Just walk a -

F♯m
F♯m(maj7)
fr4
B9
B7
Emaj7
way, just say good - bye, don't turn a - round now, you may see me
Amaj7
F♯m
F♯m♭5
cry, I must-n't fall a - part or show my bro - ken heart
C♯m
fr4
C♯7
F♯m
F♯m(maj7)
fr4
or the love I feel for you. So walk a - way and close the
B9
B7
Emaj7
door, and let my life be as it was be -

Amaj7
Dmaj7
fore. And I'll ne - ver, ne - ver know just
C♯m
B
A♯m7(♭5)
Amaj7
G♯sus4
G♯7
how I let you go but there's no - thing left to say, jnust walk a -
1.
C♯m
F♯m9
way.
Amaj7
G♯7
2.
C♯m
2. There'll -way.

F♯m
A
D7/A
Just walk a -
Gm
Gm(maj7)
C9
C7
Fmaj7
way, just say good - bye, don't turn a - round now, you may see me
B♭maj7
Gm
Gm♭5
cry, I must-n't fall a - part or show my bro - ken heart,
Dm
D7
Gm
Gm(maj7)
or the love I feel for you. So walk a - way and close the

Verse 2:
There'll never be a moment I'll regret,
I've loved you since the day we met.
For all the love you gave and all the love we made
I know I've got to find the strength to say

THE COLOUR OF MY LOVE

Words & Music by David Foster & Arthur Janov.

E♭m7
D♭add9
G♭maj7
A♭
A dim
own. I'll draw your arms a-round my waist, then all doubt I shall e-rase,
B♭m9
B♭m
A♭
G♭maj7
Fm7
B♭m7
E♭m7/A♭
I'll paint the rain that soft-ly lands on your wind blown hair,
rall.
a tempo
A♭6
I'll trace a hand to wipe your tears,
a look to calm your fears, a sil-hou-ette of dark and light, while we

G♭maj7
fr4
E♭m7/A♭
D♭
hold each oth - er oh so tight. I'll paint a
G♭maj7
fr4
Fm7
B♭m7
3
sun to warm your heart, swear - ing that we'll nev - er part,
E♭m7
fr6
E♭m7/A♭
D♭
D♭/F
that's the co - lour of my love. I'll paint the
G♭maj7
fr4
Fm7
B♭m7
3
truth, show how I feel, try to make you com - plete - ly real, I'll use a

E♭m7
Fm7
G♭maj7
/A♭
A♭
D♭
G♭/D♭
A♭/D♭
brush so light and fine to draw you close and make you mine.
D♭
Cm7add4
C7
Fmaj7
I'll paint a sun to warm your heart, swear-ing that we
Em7
Am7
Dm7
/G
G7
nev-er ev-er part, that's the co-lour of my
C
Fmaj7
love. I'll draw the years all pass-ing by, so much to

Em7
Am7
Dm7
Em7
learn, so much to try, and with this ring our lies will start,
Dm7
Em7
Dm7
Em7
swear-ing that we'll nev-er part. I of-fer what you can-not buy de-
Fmaj7
rall.
/G
G7
C
F/A
G/B
vot-ed love un-til we die,
C
F/A
G
C
F/A
G/B
C
ooh, ooh.

Unison

Words & Music by Andy Goldmark & Bruce Roberts.

C♯m
fr4
(Verse 2 see block lyric)
we come a - live,
two hearts ig - nite,
we're one of a kind
F♯m
here we are
un- di- vi - ded by
C♯m
fr4
a- ny- thing, just you and I.
We've come so far,

F♯m
G♯sus4
fr4
no one else could ev - - - er steal a - way what we con - fide.
G♯7
fr4
C♯m
fr4
Who wants to know we stick to - ge - er, we're ne - ver a - part,
A
ev - 'ry - bo - dy knows who we are, be - cause we are one,
B
C♯m
fr4
1.
we do it in u - ni - son.
2. Gleam of an eye

2.
C♯m
fr4
(in u - ni - son.) We come to - ge - ther and
A
strong-er we are just when the world can, can tear us a - part, we go
B
C♯m
fr4
on as one, we do it in u - ni - son.
We stand

Verse 2:
Gleam of an eye, flash of a smile
Never too shy, playin' ever so wild.
Here we are, I'm relying on no one else,
But you and I we've come so far
No one else could ever steal away,
What we confide, who wants to know?

The Last To Know

Words & Music by Philip Galdston & Brock Walsh.

E6
A
Dmaj7
out what I need to know. It's not that I don't think you care,
C♯m7
fr4
F♯m
E/F♯
Fmaj7
it's what you have-n't said, that keeps me guess-ing
B♭maj7
C/D
D
D
E
C♯m7
fr4
day and night put-ting vi - sions in my head. Don't let me be the
E11
E
last, don't let me be the
(If you thought of leav-ing would you tell me?)

C♯m7
fr4
E/F♯
F♯m
last or would you lie to me, don't
(If the truth would hurt me what would you say?)
Dmaj7
E6
you keep it to your-self for my pro-tec-tion, break it to me now,
F♯m
E/F♯
E11
don't let me be the last,
(If you thought of leav-ing would you tell
E6
D
C♯m7
fr4
don't let me be the last, or would you
me?) (Like you're nev-er gon-na let me go.)

Verse 2:
You know how old friends will talk
A secret's hard to keep.
But this girl she says you're seeing
Sure sounds a lot like me.
Still it's not for me to say
If what I heard was true.
And I won't let myself believe a word
Till I hear it from you.

6/97 (27956